A car stops in the road next to

Follifoot Farm. A door opens.

Two cats fall out of the car.

The car door shuts. The car speeds away. The two cats are left in a heap on the road.

Another car comes down the

road. The cats leap onto the grass

as the car speeds past them.

The cats jump up on the wall to

get away from the speeding cars.

They go along the wall to its end.

They are at a farmyard. They can see hens pecking corn by the open door of a barn.

The cats jump down into the farmyard. They go to look in the barn. They can see a big red tractor.

The cats go into the barn. They go past the big red tractor to the back of the barn.

‘Moo … oo … oooo.’ Oh no!

What is that? A cow? No. It is a

big brown bull!